Rooted in the Sky

in the

A FAITH
TO COPE
WITH CANCER

Betty Garton Ulrich

Judson Press® Valley Forge

ROOTED IN THE SKY

Copyright © 1989
Judson Press, Valley Forge, PA 19482-0851

Unless otherwise indicated, Bible quotations in this volume are from *The Holy Bible*, King James Version.

Other quotations of the Bible are from

HOLY BIBLE New International Version, copyright © 1978, New York International Bible Society. Used by permission.

The Revised Standard Version of the Bible, copyrighted 1946, 1952, ©1971, 1973 by the Division of Christian Education of the National Council of the Churches of Christ in the U.S.A., and used by permission.

The New English Bible, Copyright © the Delegates of the Oxford University Press and the Syndics of the Cambridge University Press, 1961, 1970.

The Living Bible. Tyndale House Publishers, Wheaton, Ill. Used by permission.

Good News Bible, the Bible in Today's English Version. Copyright © American Bible Society 1966, 1971, 1976.

Library of Congress Cataloging-in-Publication Data

Ulrich, Betty Garton.
  Rooted in the sky / Betty Garton Ulrich.
        p. cm.
  ISBN 0-8170-1147-1 : $7. 95
  1. Ulrich, Betty Garton—Health. 2. Colon (Anatomy)—Cancer —Patients —United States—Biography. 3. Christian life—1960- 4. Consolation. I. Title
RC280.C6A3 1989
616.99'4347'00924—dc19
[B]   89-1838
                                                                  CIP

"It is only from the light which streams constantly from heaven that a tree can derive energy to strike its roots deep in the soil. The tree is, in fact, rooted in the sky."

—*Simone Weil*[1]

"...that you, being rooted and grounded in love, may have power to comprehend with all the saints what is the breadth and length and height and depth, and to know the love of Christ..."

—*Ephesians 3:17-19 (RSV)*

To

Dr. Melvin Bubrick, surgeon;
Dr. I. Fortuny, oncologist;
Sharon Pappas, R. N., oncology assistant,

and all the unsung nurses, aides and staff
at Metropolitan Medical Center
of Minneapolis, Minnesota,

my grateful thanks!

Contents

Rooted in the Sky

Preface

MILLIONS OF PEOPLE around the world struggle with some form of cancer. I am one of them.

This book was written not because my experience is unique, but because it has reaffirmed mightily my Christian faith and given me new insights into the life and workings of the Spirit.

If one is going to be honest in trying to believe in and live by the Christian faith in a confused, puzzling, and contradictory world, hard questions arise that have no easy answers. Some books portray these problems as uncomplicated and the answers as all too simple: just believe and pray and all will come up roses, because God wants you to be healthy, wealthy and wise.

I wrote this book to explore some thinking about where God comes in—what God's role is in the areas of pain, healing, Christian growth, and the facing of this life's last act: death.

It is my hope that what I have written here will not only comfort and strengthen Christians, ill and well, but also will encourage those who have not yet committed their lives to Christ (or are having second thoughts about a previous commitment) to take a new look at his claim to be, indeed, "the Way, and the Truth, and the Life."

—*Betty Garton Ulrich*

1

Some Surprises: Bad and Good

IT WAS THE MORNING of our thirty-seventh wedding anniversary. *We've got it made,* I thought, lying in bed for a few minutes more before getting up. Five grown children who had all "turned out" well; four of them married, and to fine mates; our own retirement just a few years away.

But after breakfast, after my husband had gone to the office, the telephone rang. "The news is not good," said my doctor's voice, coming through the receiver at my ear.

"No?" I asked . . . and waited. I could sense his reluctance.

He formed his words slowly. "The X-rays show a tumor in the colon. I want to get you in touch with a specialist at once—a colorectal surgeon."

"Wait!" I said, feeling as if the world were being pulled out from under me. "I remember our daughter's mother-in-law had a wonderful surgeon. I'd like to get his name."

"Fine." The voice sounded relieved. "I have no preference, just so you get immediate attention."

"Is it—do you think it's...?" I couldn't utter the word.

"That's what we want to find out. Get that appointment immediately."

"OK," I said, more calmly than I felt. "I'll let you know what happens."

Immediately I called our daughter Ruth who is a nurse and had told me about the delicate surgery her mother-in-law had undergone two years previously. Ruth was matter-of-fact in her reaction. After all, we had already talked about this and she knew I had had X-rays. She was encouraging: "It may be benign, Mother. And if not, they seem to have found it at an early stage. They're having great success treating colon cancer."

Neither of us mentioned the fact that a close friend of our family was in the final stages of a colon cancer that had metastasized into her liver.

Ruth looked up the surgeon's name and number. I wrote it down, almost in a daze, then sat there for a moment after I hung up. I tried to collect my thoughts, compose my mind and adjust to this sudden, wrenching turn of life.

First I thought, *What an anniversary present for Bob when he comes home for lunch: "Happy anniversary, Dear...I have cancer!"*

Now wait a minute! I told myself. *Nobody has said cancer. It could be a benign tumor.* (I had always thought "benign tumor" was a contradiction in terms; now I realized how "benign" a plain tumor could seem, compared to the dreadful alternative.)

Immediately I felt an overwhelming desire to pray. And right then I had the first of what would be several surprises in connection with this new kind of experience in my life.

Because so many people we know have faced this curse of the modern western world—cancer—I had often speculated about how I would pray under such circumstances. Would the hesitation I have always had at the idea of praying for instant miracles evaporate? Would I pray that God would instantly heal me? Or slowly heal me? Or would I secretly feel that God had let me down by allowing me to get into that condition?

What did happen was that, with no premeditation, no conscious forethought about how I was going to pray, I found myself praying only that God would be present to me. What a surprise! It is difficult to describe the feeling I had. It was as if I had a terrible thirst just for God's presence. There was no thought of praying for healing, for an easing of the situation, for anything, other than God presence. The words of Psalm 42:1 came to my mind: "As the hart panteth after the water brooks, so panteth my soul after thee, O God."

I had read that verse often—sometimes almost with envy,

mingled with a bit of guilt, for the urgency of those words seemed often to highlight my own lukewarm feelings. I would think, *Do I really yearn for God like that?* The honest answer too many times was *No!*

Now I sat there, saying inside my head, "Just be here, God! Just be present. Keep me in your care!" And there came singing softly into my mind the hymn words: "God himself is with us, Let us now adore him...."

I guess I'll never be able to squelch my sense of humor entirely, for even as I was praying with all the earnestness I could command, I thought of that quote in *Boswell's Life of Samuel Johnson:* "...when a man knows he is to be hanged in a fortnight, it concentrates his mind wonderfully."[2] How true! The thought of facing an early death served wonderfully to bring priorities into sharp focus. I was amazed and gratified to discover that the overriding priority for me was simply God's presence. Bits and pieces of hymns and Scripture swirled in my mind: "If God be for us, who can be against us?" "Nothing in my hand I bring, Simply to Thy cross I cling...."

As I sat there by the telephone, a sense of peace and well-being gradually seeped through me, a sense that "the everlasting arms" truly were upholding me.

"The Lord is my shepherd," I whispered. "I shall not want." As I said the words, I knew with startling clarity what they really meant. I admit that often as I said the Twenty-third Psalm, when I came to "I shall not want," I'd have a traitorous bit of skepticism. I'd think, "But my goodness, many great Christians—and lesser ones, too—have experienced want."

I've never been one to believe that being a Christian automatically assures one of an easy, affluent road. I launch myself with the speed of a flying bullet at the television set to change channels when one of those airwave ambassadors begins assuring me that if I get into the right relationship with God, I will become rich, famous, and healthy. I know from studying the lives of departed saints (and watching the lives of living ones) that some suffer and are deprived materially—sometimes because of being Christian.

With sharpened spiritual awareness I saw that the words, "I shall not want," do not necessarily mean freedom from illness or disease or pain...even from hunger and poverty, nor even an escape, finally, from death. They are a simple acknowledgement of the promise that God's children will lack nothing necessary to see them through anything. I might be at the mercy of forces beyond my control, but whatever happened, if God is for me, who could be against me? How could Paul be so sure that nothing in all the universe could separate us from God's love? Because, as he himself put it, "I know whom I have believed, and am convinced that he is able to guard what I have entrusted to him for that Day...." (2 Timothy 1:12, NIV)

True, many people live and die with no belief—or only a very hazy one—in God. As the British say, they "muddle through" terrible crises and catastrophes, even grimly enter into death. But the Christian promise is "we are more than conquerors through him who loved us" (Romans 8:37, RSV).

What is that extra plus...that "more?" I was already experiencing part of it as I huddled silently by the telephone. I felt a presence—the Presence of the Lord, whose Spirit brings peace and calm. Incidentally, this is different from just having a "feeling" or trying to whip up a sense of God's nearness. (I've tried that, too, on occasion. It doesn't work.)

I decided to wait until my husband came home for lunch rather than call him with the news. The "sentence of hanging" would "wonderfully concentrate" his mind, too—but not on his work, which was where it belonged at the moment.

Instead, I called the surgeon's office and was given an appointment for the following Monday. This was Wednesday. They requested that I ask for my X-rays from the local hospital and bring them with me to the doctor's office in Minneapolis.

I don't remember what I did the rest of that morning, but I do remember that I seemed wrapped in that atmosphere of peace and quiet, of calmness and trust. I couldn't believe it was continuing. I waited for it to be dispelled and for fear or panic or, at the very least, a great uneasiness to take over. I even told myself, *Yeah, you're doing a great balancing act. You're carefully blocking out the reality of this thing and keeping your mind in limbo. One has the power to make oneself believe anything. You're just refusing to think about this and willing yourself to be calm.*

Deliberately, then, I let my mind focus on the "what-ifs" of my situation. What if it really is a cancerous tumor? What if it has already gone beyond control? What if it has metastasized into my liver? What if my days are already numbered? I deliberately forced myself to confront these possibilities and not flinch from the implications...in a way, almost challenging that peace of mind to prove its reality.

Immediately, in a new, never-before-experienced way, the possibility of my dying became very real to me. Most of us, to be sure, think about death, realize we'll die, and even try to imagine what it will be like. But it's all theory! It is hard to describe what happens when the imminence of death becomes a reality. I've tried to think of an analogy. The nearest I can come is to liken it to the feelings one has when the family decides to move to another city, state, or country. It may have been in the offing for a long time. It may have been discussed, considered, even acknowledged as a strong possibility.

But then, finally, the decision definitely is made, and suddenly everything is different. This city will no longer be "our" city. This house will no longer be "home." All these friends and neighbors will be left behind. And what about the new place? Will we like the new city? Will we ever find friends as dear as these?

But at best, this is a poor analogy. In an earthly move we are still a family. Our life on this earth still goes on. Plans and purposes continue. The family is together.

The reality of approaching death gives a reaction like no other, for it means the end of everything familiar, everything known and loved heretofore. One can no longer contemplate it in a philosophical, detached manner; one is soon going to enter into it...no turning back. And that point, that transition beyond life into death, is dim and shadowy.

More important, the thing had been faced, and the deep feeling of calm and of the Presence did not diminish. In this "high and stormy gale" I found I could say, in the words of that old hymn, "My anchor holds within the veil."

2

Let's Celebrate Anyway

BY THE TIME my husband was due home for lunch, I felt somewhat as if I were floating in a bubble of unreality. In a way, it frightened me that already there seemed to be an invisible barrier between me and the "real" world—as if I had somehow entered a land between this life and another dimension of the spirit. I wondered if telling Bob the news would "pop" the bubble, at the same time shattering the strange, peaceful calm that I'd been unable to budge on my own.

Wandering through the rooms I looked at the familiar objects of our household: the creaky old drop-leaf table in the dinette, covered with brightly colored stick-on plastic; the quartersawed oak cup-and-saucer rack my husband had found in a storage building at our lake place and had refinished. It hung now in the dining room, graced with six pretty, assorted cups and saucers. I looked at the tall plant rack he had made, with several circular plant holders that rotated back and forth for several inches. It was a beautiful piece of work, but too worthy for my bedraggled collection of usually ailing plants. I had to smile at his characterization of me as having "a brown thumb."

And those shelves and shelves of books in the living room, rec room, his study and mine. Many of them I'd read, but some were still on my "intended" list. Only when I thought of the books did

I get a stab of regret; maybe I'd never get a chance to read them. But all the other things I looked at were just that: things, from which I seemed already divorced. They would remain unchanged, even if I were to depart this life. It gave me a strange feeling to contemplate our possessions in such a detached way, from the perspective that they would silently remain in their places, even though I would no longer be there to water the plants or dust the books.

In the days to follow, I would notice other unaccustomed reactions. For example, I'm a great one for clipping recipes. They get stuffed into drawers, boxes, recipe files. Some of them, as my husband periodically points out to me, have never been tried out—and "why do you want to cut out more when you haven't made the ones you have?" But suddenly, my interest in collecting recipes dropped to zero. I threw out a whole box without even sorting through them.

Also, I would open a drawer to get something, then think, *That drawer is a mess! Why am I saving that stale perfume, those tag ends of dried-up lipstick?* And out they would go. The drawers were never so tidy. In short, I noticed the same syndrome that always seizes me before I go on a trip. I'd often joked about leaving the house "in dying condition." Now it wasn't a joke; it might be for real.

But on that anniversary day, wandering about the house, I finally heard my husband come in the kitchen door. When he had hung up his coat and come back into the kitchen, I said, "I hate to tell you this on our anniversary, but...well, the doctor said the X-rays show a tumor in the colon."

"Oh, no!" His face registered shock.

I nodded.

"Well," he said after a long pause, "I know this sounds funny, coming from me," (he's the kind that focuses on the hole in the donut) "but let's not borrow trouble. It could be benign."

"That's what Ruthie said."

"You've talked to her?"

"I got the name of that good surgeon and I made an appointment for next Monday."

"That's the earliest you could get?"

Again I nodded.

He sat down at the table. "It's going to be a long weekend, isn't it?"

"It'll probably seem like weeks."

He bowed his head, then raised it to look at me. "I'm going to say a special prayer before lunch."

His prayer was simple and to the point, asking that God be with us, give us courage and strength, and that I be restored to full health.

When he had finished, I confided my experience of the morning in asking only for God's presence. I added that I found it impossible for some reason to directly ask God to heal me—although I had said I wanted to live—if God didn't mind!

"I can tell God I want you healed," he said bluntly. "And I'll keep doing it."

That outright bluntness has often been a comfort to me (once I got used to it!), because you know where you stand with a person like that. It must be a valuable trait in God's eyes, too, because God knows what's in a person's heart anyway. Anything less than the blunt truth doesn't fool God.

"Now I think we still ought to celebrate our anniversary," Bob said. "How about going out for a quiet dinner and then a movie...a funny one, if there is such a thing anymore."

I agreed at once. Why sit at home and worry?

We had dinner at a small candlelit restaurant, sitting at one of several tables on a raised tier along one wall, overlooking the main dining area below. Because it was early, we were almost alone and could talk freely and softly, without having to compete with the clatter of silver and the clamor of other voices.

We began to reminisce about our life together—our early days in the ministry, the births of our five children, our summer vacations in the Wisconsin north woods, the way our children had turned out to be such fine people. I reflected to myself how, in memory, all the traumatic experiences, the quarrels, the confrontations with the children, the financial worries, the illnesses—all those "down-beat" experiences—tend to recede, leaving only the good memories foremost in one's mind. It reminded me of the biblical description of the way a woman forgets the pain of labor in her joy that a child has been born.

By now my husband was waxing truly nostalgic. "Sometimes," he said, "I wish we could bring back the days when the kids were small and we were all together. We had some great times!"

That brought me out of my nostalgic mood in a second.

"Not me!" I said, suddenly remembering the incredible exertions I had put forth caring for five children when there were no school lunch programs and I cooked three meals a day for seven people, seven days a week. I made eight loaves of bread at a time, cleaned a big parsonage, washed, ironed (before drip-dry!), walked colicky babies through the night, went through five babyhoods of potty training—and then as many teenage years trying to get them out of the bathroom!—and through it all, kept trying to "be a writer."

"The way I look at it," I told Bob, "bringing up five kids in a parsonage on low income is one of those unique experiences I'm very glad I had. But unique means 'one of a kind,' and that's my feeling exactly—once is enough!"

I started to laugh. "I feel the way our John did. Remember the time we began at a new church? John was about ten and the choir director asked if he'd like to join her junior choir. He said in his grave, polite little way, 'No, thank you. I've already been in one!'"

We both laughed and I continued, the memory so vivid in my mind, "And later, when I asked him why he'd said that, he looked so baffled, as if the reason ought to be perfectly clear. 'If you've seen one,' he explained patiently, 'you've seen 'em all.'"

We finished our meal in an anniversary mood, awash in nostalgia and much laughter.

I said, "Let's get on to that movie. We need some light entertainment to take our minds off what might be ahead. But I'll tell you one thing: if I should go tomorrow, I'd have no complaints about how life has dealt with me!"

3

*If I Should
Go Tomorrow . . .*

ON THE WAY TO THE MOVIE, my mind continued to dwell on
my past life, remembering, assessing....

I'd slid into my sixties with hardly a ripple, still active. The
years had gone by in a flash, and I'd been happy. I'd had a
wonderful, contented childhood in Indiana; beloved and loving
parents; a fine brother. I had good friends, some of whom I am still
in close contact with after more than fifty years. I had unusually
fine high school teachers, many of whom, now that I thought back
on it, were of college-instructor caliber.

My father and mother, a doctor and a nurse, had been willing to
bear the expense of sending me to an out-of-state university. At
the University of Wisconsin I was able to major in Greek and my
much-loved Latin, which I'd studied for four years in high school.

As we drove along, I remembered how, there at college, I had
become a Christian, an event that was to change my life indeed.
One might say I was "born again" before anyone was using that
phrase. It happened in my sophomore year, thanks to another
student, who to this day is like the sister I never had. Between her
and the pastor of an off-campus church, who knew how to deal
with the questions and doubts of non-Christian (and Christian!)
students, I finally came to recognize that Christ is who he said he
is. I realized then that if I wanted to know what God was like, I

need only listen, watch and learn how Jesus lived, what he said, and what he taught. It was still, though, an awful struggle to give in. I resisted, telling myself that I had too many unanswered questions about basic beliefs.

For instance, I could never just ignore the seeming contradictions between scientific theories and biblical assertions. Besides, I could use some of the conflicts as excuses to hold off from making a commitment to Christianity. After all, I had my life all planned. I loved the old cultures of Greece and Rome. I might even decide to be an archeologist. And I'd always wanted to be a writer. Life, back in those college days, spread out before me with all kinds of exciting possibilities. The sky was the limit!

But there across my path suddenly loomed this haunting Christ figure, who seemed to confront me at every turn with his "Follow me." I tried to turn a deaf ear. What if he were to lead where I didn't want to go? What if I couldn't pursue any of the paths that looked so intriguing to me? Worst of all, I was sure I couldn't be a writer, because being a Christian would narrow my horizons to the point where I wouldn't be able to write "realistically." Besides, who ever heard of a famous Christian writer? At the time I had no idea that many creative persons throughout history were motivated by their Christian faith.

It does seem a shame to think that, with all the good education I had, with all the required reading I did, nobody had pointed out that some of the world's greatest writers, poets, artists, and musicians were devout Christians. This was treated, when mentioned at all, as unimportant trivia. No one told me that Bach wrote at the end of many compositions *Soli Deo Gloria*—"To God alone be the glory"; and sometimes at the beginning *In nomine Jesu*—"in the name of Jesus." He once wrote, "The aim and end of all music should be the glory of God and the recreation of the soul." So wrote the greatest musician our world has produced. No mention of that in school! And could an unbeliever have written Handel's *Messiah*? Just the selection of biblical texts and the way they are woven together bespeak a profound knowledge and understanding of the message of the Bible.

And how about such writers as Tolstoy, Augustine, and Thomas Aquinas? How about Shakespeare, whose works are rife with Bible references? What about J.R.R. Tolkien?

Even though ignorant of all this back in those college years, I nevertheless knew that I had finally found Truth and, if I turned my back on it, I turned my back on God. So I would give up my dreams, say my "yes," and prepare to follow a new path, unexciting though it might be.

How many times since then have I laughed at my naivete! All the really exciting things that have happened to me have been because of that new path I followed. The two books and many of the articles, short stories, and the few poems that   I have had published have almost all been on Christian themes.

For four years after college, I traveled all over the United States and parts of Canada during the years of World War II, while waiting for my husband-to-be to come home from the African-Italian fronts of the war. I visited college and university campuses for five Lutheran church bodies, speaking to students, helping to start groups, leading Bible studies, retreats, etc. I discovered that although I had to make up for a woeful lack of background in Bible study itself, nevertheless, all my education in Greek and Latin, in the culture and life and times of Greece and Rome, was perfectly marvelous background for study of the Bible itself. Had God's hand been in my choice of education even before I decided to follow Christ?

I even ended up marrying a pastor—which I said I would never do. He promised me we'd never be rich but that I'd never be bored. He was so right—on both counts! He has been a faithful, good husband and father, with a sense of humor that never quite deserts him, even in his pessimistic periods. Our life has been challenging, busy and peopled with hundreds of wonderful friends.

Four of our five children, who all turned out to be beautiful Christian human beings, are married—to spouses we love. They have made us grandparents nine times over.

And then there has been "The Cabin" (to which we have now retired). Thirty years ago we fell, by what seemed absolutely a miracle, into our summer "dream place"—a large, full-log cabin, with a huge split-stone fireplace, a balcony loft, two giant, real wagon-wheel chandeliers in the living room—all in a setting of huge white and Norway pine in northern Wisconsin, on a pure, spring-fed lake. This twenty-five-acre "spread" came to us at an unbelievably low price because the owners, rather than to realize a large profit, preferred to sell it to people who would appreciate it for what it is and care for it lovingly. We got it, therefore, for the proverbial song. Over the years that couple, summering nearby on a lake connecting with ours, became like family. When the husband died in 1971, our children lost a sort of folk hero who knew all about the woods and fishing and hunting and wildlife. When his wife died at dawn on Christmas morning years later, our oldest son, Jim, married and living in Oregon, sat down and wrote a beautiful tribute to the two of them:

> Knowing the value of a dollar and yet knowing so much more, they sold my parents The Cabin. The capital letters are there because of the mythic status of the place to our family. We were always a close family: our home was wherever we were. But The Cabin and woods were really our physical home. It was always there no matter where we moved and it was always there as an image of green, cool, dark summer, as we lived out long winters in all those white, frozen cities.

Yes, that cabin is our one "place anchor" and the focal point of years of family gatherings and happy memories. My reminiscing ended as we walked into the movie theater and I told myself, *On this thirty-seventh wedding anniversary, I have so much to be thankful for; and if I should go tomorrow, I could truly say, "Thank you, God, for a lifetime of marvelous blessings!"*

4

The Miracle of Prayer

IT SEEMED AN INTERMINABLE TIME from Wednesday until Monday, the day of my appointment with the surgeon. I once wrote a humorous piece about Einstein's theory of relativity, claiming it is well understood on a practical level by anyone who has experienced doctor's orders to stay flat in bed for a week to conquer a virus. That week is infinitely longer than the week you tried to drive five thousand miles round-trip with the family to visit relatives.

The days between that Wednesday when I was told about the tumor and the following Monday felt about three weeks long! On Friday I stopped by the local hospital to pick up the X-rays which my doctor had asked them to release to me. As I approached the window of the radiology department, around the corner walked my own doctor. He took the time to stop and explain the X-rays to me, pointing out where the tumor was.

When he was all through, I said, "Doctor, the radiologist thinks it's cancer, doesn't he?"

The doctor stared at me for a long moment, then slowly, up and down, up and down, nodded his head. I felt no shock. It was as if I were receiving confirmation of some silent message my own body had already telegraphed to my subconscious mind.

I thanked him for his time and kindness and hurried home.

Should I tell my husband this or let him live the next few days in hope that I was harboring only a benign tumor? Knowing my husband, I was pretty sure he'd want to know the truth so that he would have a few days to get used to the idea before we went to see the surgeon and were sucked into the activities and tensions that would accompany preparations for surgery. Besides, I am not good at concealing things from him. I doubted if I could hold out until Monday without telling him. I needed him on the human level to uphold me.

And he did. I think we were almost closer in those few days of waiting than ever before. We were so aware that perhaps these thirty-seven years together might be the whole story. There might not be much more...or even worse, our dreams of post-retirement life together might become a nightmare of a slow and even painful end to my life, perhaps even before we reached retirement.

Our spirits were definitely beginning to sag.

And then began a continuing miracle. The news of my situation had to be imparted to the president of our church women's organization because I was scheduled to lead the January Bible study at the joint meeting of all the circles. I would have to back out because I knew either I would be preparing for surgery or recovering from it.

The minute the news was out, it spread like spilled milk. Almost immediately there was a rallying of support—cards and telephone calls assured me that I was being held in the thoughts and lifted up in the prayers of many people. The very first card came even before the appointment with the surgeon. It was typical of many that were to follow. The verse and the note enclosed by the concerned couple expressed the thought I was to hear over and over in one form or another in more than two hundred cards and notes.

The note said, "Just to let you know that we are lifting you in prayer to the wonderful healing hands of our Lord. May you know God's constant and abiding presence as you face more tests. Bless you!"

"God's constant and abiding presence"—yes, how inspired was that choice of words to describe exactly what I myself had been praying for and had already begun to experience. But the cards, the notes, and the telephone calls were not the whole story. There was something more...and it's hard to explain. It's like trying to describe something that in essence is really indescribable. It isn't imagination. It isn't just "a feeling," although it certainly affects one's feelings. What really does happen when intercessory prayer is employed? Certainly great Christians of every age have not only advocated it, but have practiced it. For years I, too, have prayed for others, not quite sure exactly how it worked, but believing it does work because God's Word says so.

Now I know from my own experience at least part of the answer. I'm convinced that somehow prayer sets in motion and releases spiritual power that surrounds and bears up the one being prayed for. It is as if an unseen but very real Presence is there, radiating peace and calm security—yes, even a sense of joy.

I repeat, this is not something that one just "whips up" in one's own mind. It's more like an invasion of Something Other—call it what you will: a spiritual force, a loving Presence, whatever. I call it the promised Comforter—God's Holy Spirit—who comes with especially strong power in answer to the prayers of the faithful. This experience was the same as when I had prayed myself for God's presence that morning by the telephone. But now it seemed to be increased, sustained, abiding, through no effort of my own, but because of the prayers of many, many people: prayers that were being raised in my behalf. It was actually exhilarating, and periodically I would experience unexplained, brief flashes of sheer joy. Strange...but wonderful!

Monday finally came and, armed with my X-rays, my husband and I kept the appointment with the surgeon. Usually I think of myself as about twenty years younger than I really am, but I knew I was over the hill when my first thought upon seeing him was, "Oh, he's so young!"

However, from having studied while awaiting his entrance all of the certificates of membership in professional societies, diplomas, and degrees hanging on his walls, I realized from their dates that he must be at least in his early forties. He came in quietly but quickly—a very thin man with a level, dark-eyed, discerning stare.

I received two immediate, seemingly contradictory impressions: one, of an intense, efficient, maybe even perfectionist type of person; the other, of a very sensitive, truly caring individual. I was to discover later that those impressions, whether contradictory or not, were both true. In addition, he had that elusive quality of being able to inspire almost immediate confidence in a patient.

He sat down behind his desk and said, "Well, since I know nothing about you, you'll have to fill me in. Through what connection did you come to me?"

I explained that our daughter was a nurse in the same hospital in which he did surgery and described the rather unusual bit of surgery he had performed on her mother-in-law two years previously. He immediately remembered and even mentioned the name of the other specialist who had been involved in that operation.

Then he asked what symptoms had prompted me to seek medical help and I answered, "My only symptom was blood in the stools. That sent me to my own doctor, resulting in the X-rays which showed the tumor."

"I'm going to go have a look at those X-rays, then we'll examine you and then we'll talk. OK?"

I said, "My husband is out there in the waiting room. Could he be in here when we talk?"

"By all means—he should be in on this."

The doctor was gone several minutes. My eyes wandered back to his framed certificates. I noticed that one of his degrees was from the University of Wisconsin at Madison, my own alma mater. That gave me an obscure sense of confidence.

A nurse came and led me to an examining room for a proctoscopic examination. There is probably no more degrading position than the one necessary for this examination! One kneels on the footrest of the examining table, the bottom half of which is in lowered position. Then the table is tipped until one's head points floorward and one's derrière is elevated. But the exam itself was not nearly so uncomfortable nor painful as I had heard.

Afterward, I returned to the doctor's office where he rejoined me, followed by my husband.

The doctor came right to the point: "Well, we have a problem, but it's something we can do something about. You're lucky you had symptoms to alert you."

His manner was so assured that my spirits lifted at once.

"You do have a cancerous tumor in the colon; but its size seems to indicate that it has been caught fairly early. It's far enough up from the rectum that I can get it and reconnect the colon without your having to have even a temporary colostomy."

He pulled out a postcard-size illustration of the colon/rectal area and pointed to where the tumor was. "You're fortunate," he said, "as to its location. If it had been over on the other side, it could have remained undetected for a long time. While I was doing the exam, I also did a biopsy. I want to know what kind of cancer we're dealing with. It might give me an advantage in operating." (He later told me that if I had to have cancer, mine was the "best" kind.)

His whole manner was so confident, so assured, that I felt completely at ease and sure that all would be well. I realized the truth of what I had often read: the attitude of the doctor and the patient's confidence in the doctor are big factors in the healing process.

Before he came back into the office, he evidently had told a woman in the outer office to make arrangements for my admission to the hospital, for he now said, "I'm having you admitted on Thursday and we'll have the surgery on Friday. And, if you don't mind, I'd like to have one of our internists give you a complete physical. OK?"

I liked the low-key way he approached things: not, "Now, we're going to do so-and-so," but, "If you don't mind...." I agreed; I'd been one of those foolish people who had not had a complete physical for years because I "felt so good." I realize now how important periodic physical checkups are, especially for older people. If my tumor, as the doctor said, had been on the other side, far up into the colon, I could have had no symptoms until it was so far advanced that other organs could have been involved. Incidentally, there is a simple test which can be performed at home that will indicate the presence in the stool of "occult" (hidden) blood.

The doctor's receptionist appeared at the door. "I'm sorry, Doctor, but they say they can't schedule any more this week—it'll have to be sometime next week."

My heart sank—more waiting! The doctor's face barely changed expression, but he said very quietly, "Oh, yes, they can. You tell them to schedule her for Friday—I'll do some juggling of my own schedule."

The receptionist disappeared and the doctor said to me, "Your surgery will be Friday, but we'll have to let you know the time later." I did not tell him that my packed bag already was in the car, so that had he decided on immediate admittance, we would not have to make the sixteen-mile trip home across the Twin Cities and back again.

The next evening, Tuesday, was to mark the last regular meal I would eat for over a week. Total clean-out was now the goal, beginning with a diet on Wednesday of clear liquids, gelatin the most "solid" food permitted.

Somehow, I wasn't very hungry anyway and awaited Thursday morning with a mixture of hope, trepidation, and the thought, phrased humorously in a saying my mother had often quoted ever since I was a little girl: "What is to be will be, whether it ever comes to pass or not."

Wednesday I was to drink ten ounces of magnesium citrate—oh, boy! It tastes like lemonade, but that's as far as the resemblance goes. After drinking it, one had better stay home, with a clear shot to the bathroom!

Meanwhile, the cards, notes and telephone calls continued pouring in. I could not escape making a direct correlation between the constant prayers of many people and the steady, quiet oasis of peace and confidence that held firm despite moments of apprehension. Those moments when a deep sense of joy would pass through me were totally inexplicable apart from the influence of that upholding power breaking through from the spiritual dimension into the physical arena.

In the days to come, I was to experience even more remarkable evidences of the strength of this power.

5

The Final Countdown

THURSDAY MORNING we were up early—no breakfast for
me—and then into the car for the thirty-minute drive across the
Twin Cities to the imposing bulk of a building that is the Metropolitan Medical Center. MMC is an amalgamation of two old
hospitals, Swedish and St. Barnabas. It is now also connected to
Hennepin County General Hospital across the street by a huge,
covered walkway overarching the road. My husband has often
remarked, not entirely in jest, that he's afraid of the whole place.
He claims it's so vast that a patient could easily be mislaid and
languish in some corner on one of those abominable carts for days.

It may be huge and look frighteningly impersonal, but the inside
is filled with concerned, caring people—just how caring was
another surprise in store for me.

Admitting took only a few minutes and almost at once I was
being ushered into—well, well!—a private room. We hadn't asked
for that, but I was happy that I would be alone. Knowing that the
"cleaning out" process would continue apace that day, I had
worried about a tied-up bathroom—or a roommate's hordes of
chattering and/or smoking visitors. This was nice and peaceful.

Almost immediately, while I was still dressed, a dark-haired,
energetic doctor (another young-looking one!) made his appearance and introduced himself as the internist who was to do the

physical exam.

He began with questions, my answers to which he recorded on a form. He seemed mildly surprised that my only hospitalization in my whole life (except for the births of five children) had been a tonsillectomy at age five and a brief bout with pneumonia in college. Aside from measles, mumps, chicken pox, and whooping cough, my only illness had been a strep infection of the blood-stream when I was a child, before the discovery of antibiotics. My parents, a doctor and a nurse, had cared for me at home. No heart trouble, no diabetes, no high blood pressure, no arthritis—nothing. And no, I said, in answer to his question, I had never smoked and was on no medication except vitamins.

Then he asked me how old my parents were when they died and what caused their deaths.

"Oh," I said, "my mother is still living."

He glanced down at his record—I presumed to recheck my age—then said, "Still living? How old is she?"

"Over ninety-two," I replied, "and sharp enough mentally to beat me at Scrabble and remember all kinds of stuff I forget."

He looked a bit startled, then asked, "And your father?"

"He died a couple of years ago—but we don't know the actual cause of his death. He was out fishing and was found drowned. He soon would have been eighty-five. He was younger than my mother."

As the doctor rose to step out of the room so that I could prepare for the exam by donning one of those dreadful, short hospital gowns with the gaping back, he said, "I wish I were from your family!"

I gathered that longevity was not a prominent genetic trait in his family.

During the ensuing physical, he repeatedly exclaimed about what great condition I was in, until finally I felt compelled to say, "Doctor, if I'm in such great shape, what am I doing here?"

He just laughed. "Well," he said, "you ought to come through surgery just fine!"

When he had gone, I lay quietly, thinking about my situation and experiencing the sort of fatalistic, "the-die-is-cast" feeling one gets on leaving the high dive at the pool or at the onset of labor in childbearing: it's in the works—there's no going back.

Such philosophizing was cut short by the entrance of a nurse with a small cup of liquid.

"Drink it right down," she instructed cheerily. "It's quite salty."

"It" turned out to be the final potion in the noble attempt to get me totally cleaned out. I remember that during the hours from about 3 to 5 A.M. the next morning, I must have made that sprint to the bathroom about fifteen times. I told my husband that, on reflection, it was rather disconcerting to realize what a large percentage of humans is evidently waste matter.

When I went in on Thursday, they had informed me that my surgery was scheduled for 1:30 P.M. the next day. That meant another half day without food or drink, for beginning at midnight not even water was to pass my lips. I viewed this prospect with more apprehension than I did the surgery. It's strange how we Americans count on three square meals a day and view the possibility of missing even one—let alone two or three days' worth—as a near calamity. At least I knew I would be eating full meals in a short time. I thought of all the people in the world who don't know what or when their next meager meal will be.

I found, strangely, that I was not even hungry, or thirsty, despite my conviction that every bit of flowable matter had been drained out. My body seemed to be in a quiescent state, demanding nothing, expecting nothing.

Before I went to sleep that night, I opened my Bible. Some pages in my own handwriting were taped in the front. When I knew I was going to the hospital, I had flown into a flurry of "putting the house in order"—particularly my study, which tends to lie buried most of the time under piles of manuscripts, books, correspondence, articles and newspaper clippings waiting to be filed, periodicals, and numerous memos written to myself on assorted sizes and colors of scrap paper.

As I was sorting and restacking my piles, I had come across several pieces of small note paper, the top sheet of which was headed, "Night Caps." I began to smile at the memories those pages called up. A couple of years previously I had led a retreat of our church women. As a climax to the opening session on Friday evening, I had startled the ladies by saying, "We want all of you to have a good night's sleep so you will be fresh and alert for tomorrow's sessions. Therefore, I want to give you each a sedative—a sleeping pill."

There were puzzled, apprehensive, and embarrassed looks as I

What a wonderful idea

went around the circle, reaching into a brown paper bag and handing each lady a capsule.

As I passed them out, I said, "Now, don't panic. You don't swallow these. Instead, when you're all ready for bed, take the capsule apart. Inside you will find a rolled-up piece of paper. Typed on that ribbon of paper is a verse or two from the Bible, mostly from Psalms. Read it slowly and thoughtfully, and I guarantee that it will give you a sense of peace and calm and you will drift off to sleep relaxed and secure in the Lord's care."

Cleaning my study, I had rediscovered the "master list" and realized that these verses were, in the aggregate, very powerful. I then had taped them to the inside front cover of my Bible.

I was looking at the list in the hospital that night before my surgery. I include the list here because I think it contains powerful medicine for anyone, whether facing a crisis or not. Reading a few verses—or all of them—at bedtime ought to soothe and calm anyone and induce a quiet and restful sleep. This would also be a welcome list for a friend or fellow church member who is going in for surgery, or even for someone who has trouble going to sleep.

NIGHT CAPS

1. The Lord answered, "I will go with you in person and set your mind at rest" (Exodus 33:14, NEB).

2. I lie awake at night thinking of you—of how much you have helped me—and how I rejoice through the night beneath the protecting shadow of your wings (Psalm 63:6-8, LB).

3. O God my Strength! I will sing your praises, for you are my place of safety. My God is changeless in his love for me and he will come and help me (Psalm 59:9-10a, LB).

4. Yes, he alone is my Rock, my rescuer, defense and fortress. Why then should I be tense with fear when troubles come? (Psalm 62:2, LB).

5. Give your burdens to the Lord. He will carry them. He will not permit the godly to slip or fall. (Psalm 55:22 LB)

6. You have seen me tossing and turning through the night...This one thing I know: God is for me! I am trusting God—oh, praise his promises! (Psalm 56:8-10, LB).

7. I am poor and needy, yet the Lord is thinking about me right now! O my God, you are my helper (Psalm 40:17, LB).

8. Oh, praise the Lord, for he has listened to my pleadings! He

is my strength, my shield from every danger (Psalm 28:6-7a, LB).

9. I will bless the Lord who counsels me; he gives me wisdom in the night. He tells me what to do (Psalm 16:7, LB).

10. Lie quietly upon your bed in silent meditation. Put your trust in the Lord...I will lie down in peace and sleep...O Lord, you will keep me safe! (Psalm 4:4b, 5a, 8; LB).

11. In my distress I screamed to the Lord for his help. And he heard me from heaven; my cry reached his ears...He led me to a place of safety, for he delights in me...He fills me with strength and protects me wherever I go (Psalm 18:6, 19, 32, LB).

12. Be delighted with the Lord. Then he will give you all your heart's desires. Commit everything you do to the Lord. Trust him to help you do it and he will...Rest in the Lord; wait patiently for him to act (Psalm 37:4, 5, 7a, LB).

13. Don't fret and worry—it only leads to harm. But all who humble themselves before the Lord shall be given every blessing, and shall have wonderful peace (Psalm 37:8b, 11, LB).

14. I waited patiently for God to help me; then he listened and heard my cry...he steadied me as I walked along. He has given me a new song to sing, of praises to our God (Psalm 40:1-3, LB).

As I read those verses that night in the hospital, that strange calm, that aura of peace and composure seemed to pervade my being and the whole room. It was as if Someone Unseen were nearby, emanating the essence of that peaceful ambience. I slept well.

The next morning a nurse came in and explained that I would be taken down about 11:30 A.M. because my surgery had been rescheduled from 1:30 to 12:30. I quickly called my husband to come an hour earlier.

Our middle child, the nurse, Ruth, came to sit with her father during the surgery, and their encouraging faces were hovering over me as I was wheeled to the "prep" room outside the operating room. I learned later that our son-in-law came also, after I was in the operating room, and sat with them until it was over.

Meanwhile, I had already been given something that was putting me into a most relaxed condition. In the prep room another strange thing happened, as if God were bent on giving me even more tangible evidence of being present with me. I was wheeled into a vacant space next to a large man, and somebody pulled the curtain around the oval ceiling tracks, closing me in. A bright light came on and a lovely-faced lady greeted me and proceeded to "prep" me. She was swift and sure and it took less than a minute. She pulled the sheet blanket up over me, turned out the bright light and then, instead of leaving, she came to the head of the cart, took one of my hands in both of hers and leaning down close said very softly, "I just want you to know that I pray for every patient I prep. While you are in there, I'll be praying that you have a good operation and a rapid recovery."

She straightened up, and I am sure that had I only nodded and smiled or said, "Thank you," she would have departed quietly, leaving it at that. But I was so taken with the glow that shone from her face that, I said, "You must be a Christian!"

A great smile lit her face and she said, "I am!"

I smiled back and said, "Me, too...and thanks so much!"

She squeezed my hand. "I'll be praying for you!"

Then she moved to the foot of the cart, opened the curtains fully and walked away. I could see her across the big room, a lovely smile on her face. She had washed her hands and was drying them. She looked across at me, nodded and smiled reassuringly, then moved off toward another patient.

Somebody was moving my cart, and I was wheeled into surgery, feeling my face wreathed in a peaceful smile.

6

Relinquishment

ALTHOUGH MY SURGEON had been reassuring about the good prognosis, still a person cannot face major surgery without also facing the fact that one may not survive. Also, once that word "cancer" has been used to describe your ailment, you instinctively react on the basis of all the stories you have heard, all the people you have known who went through the agonizing struggles with debilitating chemotherapy and who finally "didn't make it." Because my husband is a minister, we have probably known more than our share of these.

Thus one is brought face-to-face with the prospect of perhaps having to say farewell to everyone, everything that one knows and is a part of and to confront the Great Unknown.

Elisabeth Kubler-Ross became famous with her book *On Death and Dying* [3] in which she detailed the five stages a dying person goes through. I remember that three of those stages were anger, depression, and, at last, acceptance. I did not experience anger or depression—primarily, I'm sure, because I had no sentence of death passed on me by a doctor. On the contrary, the prognosis was most hopeful. Nevertheless, I thought about those "stages," and I could understand them perfectly: anger would be a logical emotion on the part of a person who doesn't want to relinquish life. Someone who enjoys life would rebel at the very thought, unless, of course, there has been so much illness and suffering that death becomes a preferred alternative. Even then, such people, before arriving at that point, have probably long ago gone through the preceding "stages." But normally, most people do not want life to end. We do not look forward to bidding a final farewell to family and friends. Who would not quail at the thought of being propelled by forces beyond one's control into permanent exile from all that has been known and held dear? One natural human response would certainly be anger.

Then, I suppose, as you keep facing the inevitable and come more fully to realize that absolutely nothing you can do will change the course of events, a natural transition would be from anger to depression. You still don't want to accept, but there is nothing to be done. In discussing these emotions, I hope no one misreads these paragraphs and concludes that I think no "real" Christian would have these feelings. No matter how strongly one might believe in the life to come, the wrench of leaving this life is very real. Christians, just like anyone else, have to work through the negative reactions. Of course, temperaments vary also. Some people are more able than others to bring these deep feelings to the surface and deal with them. But Christianity, with its endless resources and vibrant promises, certainly ought to help its adherents deal more effectively with the trauma of death than those who have no faith, no hope of eternity, and who have to believe that this life is all there is.

Incidentally, there's a lot of what seems to me to be a false optimism about death. Some people talk about it as "just a natural part of life—the final stage in the life cycle." Some try to paint death as wonderful, the doorway through which one passes into a blissful eternal life...automatically. That is not what the Bible teaches. It talks about death as "the last enemy." It talks about death as "the wages of sin." And certainly it does not talk about death as the automatic prelude to eternal bliss. Instead, the New Testament talks about Christ as the Savior from the eternal separation from God that will be the fate of those who refuse to hear and respond to God's call.

So, whatever we think about it, however much we discuss it, in the end death comes to us all. In the "stages" of reaction, according to Dr. Kubler-Ross, the final one is acceptance—the bowing to the inevitable.

As I thought about all this, I realized that, in a Christian context, all these stages that Kubler-Ross talks about are steps in a single process: learning to relinquish. A great contemporary saint of the Christian church for whom I once worked said, "Christians must learn to hold their blessings in open hands." I assume he meant that Christianity at its highest—and at its basis, for that matter— is the art of relinquishment.

Come to think of it, what is the first thing Christianity demands of its adherents? Isn't it the giving up of the claim to oneself? "...it is no longer I who live, but Christ who lives in me," Paul explains in Galatians 2:20 (RSV).

Our great example, the epitome of relinquishment, is Christ himself, who "always had the nature of God, but he did not think that by force he should try to become equal with God. Instead of this, of his own free will he gave up all he had, and took the nature of a servant. He became like man and appeared in human likeness. He was humble and walked the path of obedience all the way to death—his death on the cross" (Philippians 2:6-8, GNB).

As I went through the process I've described—that of facing the possibility that this event might be the beginning of the end for me—I received another surprise: I found myself shifting gears, so to speak, in my mind. I began to adjust emotionally and psychologically to the giving up of dreams, hopes, loved ones, loved places—all life itself as I have known and do know it. It also surprised me that I was experiencing no rebellion against these thoughts—sadness, yes...reluctance, yes...the hope that I would have a long life span as both my parents have had, yes. But no anger, rebellion or depression.

Why? I asked myself. *Am I abnormal? Is my subconscious making me block out reality?*

Then I began to think more specifically about the art of relinquishment and realized what had been happening to me for the last forty years. It began with that first relinquishment of self when I asked the Lord of Life to replace my will with divine will, to replace my claim to my life with God's own rightful and prior claim.

Over the years, every time I came to God in humility and contrition for my sins, I was relinquishing my human pride. Whenever, during those forty years, I personally, or we as a family, followed our perception of God's will instead of our own, we were relinquishing our claims to our "rights," our "natural" desires, in order to please our heavenly Father. When we relinquished ourselves by giving up our time, money or personal convenience to help others and to show love, I learned that God's way was always for our own good, so that I never, in the end, felt that I was "giving up" a greater good for a lesser, or "sacrificing" for God's sake. But the point is, we had to relinquish before God could give us those blessings.

Again, I emphasize that I don't want to lay a guilt trip on any Christian by seeming to imply that, if you're a Christian, you will not ever have feelings of rebellion, anger or depression if faced with death. I'm only reporting my own experience and what I learned. Someone else might have to work through much agony to arrive at the point of relinquishment.

Lived as God wills, the Christian life is in a very real sense a preparation for death...the final relinquishment. During the course of our Christian living we discover that each relinquishment paves the way for more spiritual growth and added blessings. In the same way, I could see now that the willingness to relinquish this life itself is not only a logical corollary to all those smaller relinquishments, but it is also the path to a brave and fearless transition from this limited sphere of being into a new environment. This new condition is so wonderful that Paul is moved to say in Second Corinthians that he would "much prefer to leave our body and be at home with the Lord." That "home" is beautifully described in Revelation as a city that

> ...has no need of the sun or the moon to shine on it, because the glory of God shines on it, and the Lamb is its lamp. The peoples of the world will walk by its light, and the kings of the earth will bring their wealth into it. The gates of the city will stand open all day; they will never be closed, because there will be no night there" (Revelation 21:23-25, GNB).

When the full realization struck me of how relinquishment in the life of the Christian is the path that leads to this final consummation, I could only stand in awe at the marvelous work God had been doing in me without my even being aware of it...for forty years.

I couldn't help but think, "Oh, I wish I could get across to all people everywhere that this is what life is really all about—not a race for power, prestige, money, not a chance to chase pleasure and personal satisfaction in material things,but a chance to become more like God; to grow into seeing things from God's point of view; to prepare for citizenship in that eternal kingdom where "...death shall be no more, neither shall there be mourning nor crying nor pain any more, for the former things have passed away." (Revelation 21:4, RSV).

At this point I can hear someone saying, "But is relinquishment and resignation all that good? It's said that people who have a great will to live, a determination that they are going to make it, have a better chance of survival. If I became very ill and just decided to relinquish and not fight for life, maybe I'd die sooner."

Here again, I think there's a third alternative to either grimly struggling against death or just giving up and not trying to live. Christianity offers another choice that is something of a paradox, as is often the case with the Christian faith. It is perfectly possible for a Christian to have a strong will to live, yet at the same time be willing to die, if that appears inevitable.

But such a paradoxical attitude can be best exhibited, and perhaps only fully exhibited, by a Christian. *Certainly, I thought, it must be very hard for a person who has spent his or her whole life pursuing personal gain and personal pleasure to face that final relinquishment of life itself without having had any practice along the way in the lesser relinquishments.*

It is amazing to me how many Bible passages that I felt I understood have struck me with new and deeper meaning: "Whoever loses his life for my sake will save it, but whoever insists on keeping his life will lose it" (Luke 9:24, LB). If your lifetime is spent "saving" your life, that is protecting your own interests, withholding yourself from the needs of others, making yourself the center of your own life, then, says Jesus, you will lose your life. I take that now to mean that you will have lost the chance to know what real life is: life lived in and for Christ, life that is rich in those elements of deep joy, peace, and certainty that come when the Spirit is invisibly present with divine gifts and guidance.

Of course, no matter how late in life one calls on the Almighty in true humility and repentance, God answers; God comes, but what an advantage in a time of deep crisis to have been in God's presence for years, to know whom you believe, to have God's Word and way so much a part of your life that in the crisis you turn naturally, trustingly to the One who is a Friend of long-standing, whose voice you have been familiar with for ever so long a time.

I've always remembered a short article from one of our Fort Wayne, Indiana, papers when I was growing up, about Mark Twain, whose real name was Samuel Clemens.

As a young man, Samuel Clemens fell in love with and married a beautiful Christian girl named Livy. After their marriage she wanted to maintain her custom of a family altar and prayer at meals. For a time Clemens went along with it.

Finally one day he said, "Livy, you can go on by yourself with this if you want to. But leave me out. I don't believe in your God and you're only making a hypocrite out of me."

Gradually, under the influence of her unbelieving mate, Livy Clemens slowly grew further and further away from her early devotion to her Lord. Meanwhile, the writings of Samuel Clemens, under the pen name of Mark Twain, brought fame and affluence. Sam and Livy were welcomed into the royal courts of Europe. They were flying high and life seemed wonderful.

But then came a day of deep trouble and Samuel said, "Livy, if your Christian faith can help you now, turn to it."

She replied, "I can't, Sam. I haven't any. It was destroyed a long time ago."

7

Under the Knife

I WAS UNDER THE SURGEON'S KNIFE for four hours and twenty minutes. They have evidently changed some hospital procedures since I had our five babies. There were no bright lights glaring into my face as I was placed on the operating table. They must have turned them on after I was anesthetized. The room was warm and quiet. All I noticed were the movements and soft voice of the anesthesiologist.

That's the last I remember, until I floated hazily back into semiconsciousness and heard myself muttering, "Oh, the pain! The pain!"

The faces of my daughter and husband hovered dimly above me. My daughter said, "Sure, Mom...you had a lot of surgery." She told me the surgery had lasted until 5:30 P.M.

I felt myself being wheeled into some other room and lined up inside a cubicle. They must have given me a shot, because the pain subsided. I was aware of the presence of my daughter and husband. I drifted into and out of consciousness, then knew that they were gone. I had no sense of whether it was day or night. I slept and woke, slept and woke. I found I was unable to lie on either side for more than an hour. I have a hunch that the struggles I went through hourly to get maneuvered onto my back, then, most laboriously, onto the other side were partially responsible for the fact that I was able to get out of bed the first day without any pain and walk down the hall.

When I "came to" enough in the cubicle to be more aware, I realized there was a tube down my nose into my stomach. Nothing, not even saliva, was to pass through my stomach and enter the colon for three days, at least.

I also discovered later that I sported a catheter, which I did not feel at all. But that nose tube was a pain...literally. It irritated my nose and made one side of my throat sore.

There was a big clock on the wall. I remember waking up over and over, thinking I had slept for hours, only to see that about one hour had passed. Then I would begin the arduous process of hoisting to my other side.

During those hours in the recovery room that first night, another of those strange, unexplainable episodes happened that by now I almost had come to expect. Except this one began differently and frightened me. I had just come awake once more and was trying to turn over. As I finally rolled over, a great, sinking sensation engulfed me—not pain, just a feeling of a great gulf beneath me, a great void and sense of aloneness. I've never before experienced exactly that feeling—except, I remembered hazily, the time I was wrestling, way back during my college days, with the claims of Christianity. I had come face-to-face with what the rest of my life would be like if I really voted for no God, no eternity—nothing but my own pitiful resources—then I'd had this same sinking, bottomless-pit sensation. Having it now frightened me. Was God deserting me? Had I been imagining God's presence? Was the whole Christian experience a mirage, a delusion? Or could this be something like what Christ had experienced, a million times more intensely, when he cried out, "My God, my God! Why have you forsaken me?"

I tried to pray, but I couldn't get any words together. Finally I cried out in my mind, *God, let there be somebody awake, praying for me!* Almost immediately that sense of deep peace and a quiet Presence enfolded me, and I slipped easily back into sleep.

Later, one of the women from church told me she had wakened in the night after my surgery and, feeling ill at ease, had begun to pray for me. She didn't know what time it had been; and I, turned away from the big clock on the wall, had not known what time I awoke with that lost feeling and had asked that somebody be praying. I like to believe there was a connection.

Thinking back on that experience, I remember reading a piece by a Christian writer who referred to the times when we seem totally unable to pray. Those, she said, are the times we must trust to the prayers of our brother and sister Christians to hold us up before the throne of grace and pray the prayers we are unable to utter. .

Sometime the next morning I was wheeled back into a regular room and, to my great joy, I found that it was the same room I'd had before. It seemed like home!

Over by the window there were two shelves. In the following days those shelves were filled with gorgeous plants and bouquets so beautiful that a nurse said, "Oh, will you leave your door open? It gives all of us a lift just to see that 'garden' as we pass by."

Promptly upon my arrival back in my room, I was hooked up to an IV bag with another bag of something piggy-backed onto the IV tube. So I had a total of four tubes busily transporting input and outgo. Turning over became even more of a challenge. But, oh, the bliss of having that bed which one could, at the touch of a button, elevate at head or knees. It is amazing how just an inch or two up or down relieves the strain on muscles and tisues that have been in one position too long.

That first morning, fairly early I think, the surgeon appeared at my bedside, obviously fresh from the operating room, still attired in a blue, v-necked top with a white coat thrown over it. He is very thin anyway, and this morning he looked almost cadaverous, and very, very tired. But he was as kind and gentle and patient as ever. He explained in detail what he had done in the surgery.

"The tumor," he said, "was bigger than we had thought. It had grown through the wall of the colon and was resting against an ovary; so we took the ovaries and tubes." He smiled slightly. "Figured you wouldn't be needing those any more." (Later, when I told my husband this, he joked, "Oh, boy! How sad! Now we can't have any more kids." I told that gray, grinning grandfather, "Get lost!")

"However," the doctor went on, "that ovary was absolutely clean. I usually remove several surrounding lymph nodes since it's quite normal to find that seven or eight or more nodes near a tumor can be infected. But with you, I removed twenty-one nodes to be safe. After testing, we found that only the one nearest the site of the tumor was involved. While I was in there anyway, I took the appendix and fixed a hernia."

"So you think you got it all?" I was almost afraid to ask, but his description sounded encouraging.

"It seems so," he said. "I checked the liver carefully and it looked OK. However, no one can say with one-hundred percent confidence that there isn't some stray cancer cell floating around somewhere. So we recommend some preventive treatment. But we'll talk about that later. Right now, you just get well—you came through surgery fine and you're doing great."

Out he went and in came a nurse to ask cheerily if I would like to try sitting up on the edge of the bed.

I really wouldn't, I thought. But I knew that getting patients up immediately is important to prevent pneumonia. So up I got, feeling like a puppet with all those plastic "strings" attached to various parts of my anatomy.

On the next day, I ventured forth, clutching that coat-rack-on-wheels that suspends the IV bags, and being clutched by a helpful nurse. I walked about thirty or forty feet to where a yellow trash basket stood. The nurse said, "Do you want to try for those big windows over there and look out?"

"No," I said weakly, surveying the approximately forty more feet. "I think not."

"That's OK," she said. "You need to remember, you'll have to go back as far as you come!"

I tottered back and fell—well, eased—gratefully into bed, with due regard for my various tubes.

My mother, who had been a nurse, wrote me from Arizona, "It's wonderful what they do these days. Post-operative patients used to be kept in bed for ten days; and then they ended up with pneumonia and a mess of adhesions!"

Speaking of preventing complications, they do have interesting methods of keeping the lungs cleared—interesting but aggravating. While I was still in the recovery room, they wheeled in this big machine with a hose that had a mouthpiece. The patient must blow into this, against an air pressure that is blowing back! It was brought in once or twice a day for the duration of my stay. I hated it and learned to outwit its tendency to strangle me: I stuck my tongue into the aperture until I could draw another breath and fight back.

In between this daily ordeal, there was always another little gadget that remained with me. I was admonished by the nurses to use it several times a day. It was a little plastic gismo, perhaps a foot high and big enough to hold a Ping-Pong ball. It also had a hose and mouthpiece, and the trick this time was to inhale through the mouth with enough force to make the Ping-Pong ball leap upward to touch the base of a moveable plunger, which could be adjusted up or down. This, they explained, was to force the air deep down into my lungs and keep them aired out.

Later when our three-year-old grandson, Jason, came with his mother to visit me, he was captivated and wanted to blow on the gadget. I explained that he was just getting over a cold, and the doctor didn't want anyone but me to use it. However, a nurse informed me afterwards that I had paid for it and could take it home if I wished. *A unique present for little Jason,* I thought.

In this recounting of the first day after surgery, it sounds as if I were "back to normal." Far from it! The anesthetic was no doubt stll wearing off, because I remember that when my husband came to sit with me that Saturday I kept falling asleep.

Once I said, "Have I been dozing? Sorry to keep dropping off like this, right in your face."

"That's OK," he said. "I can stand a little rest myself."

He held my hand and no doubt he dozed, too.

What was most surprising, though, was that after those first few moments of pain upon my regaining consciousness, I experienced thereafter no pain at all, not even intermittent twinges. At first, I thought nothing of it, assuming this was normal. But that first night back in my own room, a nurse slipped in. She tiptoed over and peered down at me.

"I'm awake," I said.

"I just came to see if you'd like a pain pill."

I shook my head. "I don't have any pain."

She looked at me a moment, then nodded and disappeared.

The next night another nurse appeared in the middle of the night and, finding me awake, asked the same question.

Again I said, "No, thanks—I don't have any pain." Then I added, "In fact, I haven't had any pain except for a few minutes right after I came out of surgery."

The nurse looked at me with a puzzled frown, then disappeared. I heard her outside my door, flipping through the pages of my chart.

In a moment she was back, leaning over my bed. "Do you know," she asked, "what all you had done to you?"

I nodded. "The doctor told me: an eighteen-inch colon resection, removal of twenty-one lymph nodes, ovaries, tubes, appendix and repair of a hernia."

She nodded gravely. "And you don't have any pain?"

"That's right," I said. "No pain."

She looked so skeptical that I felt compelled to add, "Listen, I'm no martyr! If I had pain, I'd be yelling for a pill, believe me!"

She still looked slightly doubtful, shook her head in apparent bafflement, patted my shoulder and departed.

I got my next clue that this was not the normal course of events when the wife of the man in the room next to mine stopped in my doorway and said, "Pardon me, but are you the lady that hasn't had any pain after major surgery?"

Later I asked two nurses in our congregation if people usually have pain after such surgery. Both assured me that most people certainly do. Again, I could only attribute my lack of pain to the constant prayers of so many people, plus the effects of the great calm and peace in which I seemed to have been wrapped from the beginning.

However, I learned much later of another pertinent factor. Months afterward, our oldest son, living in Oregon, told me that he knew what time my surgery was to be and, during that time, he settled down to deep prayer. In the course of it, Jim said, he asked God if "I could please take Mother's pain myself."

As he remained in prayer, he said, pain suddenly wracked his abdomen. "It didn't damage anything," he assured me. "It didn't affect my health. It just pained!"

I have no way of knowing what really happened there—whether God granted his request, or whether he had "sympathetic" pain. I only know that he is not an unstable nor excitable young man. He's very "laid back," but sensitive and intelligent. And, in addition, I know that I had no pain. The only other explanation is that it just "happened"—which really isn't much of an explanation at all, is it?

8

Healing Laughter

*"...God has given us wit, and flavor, and brightness, and
laughter to enliven the days of man's pilgrimage, and to
charm his pained steps."*
                                       —Sydney Smith[4]

WHAT A BIG PART humor and laughter played in my experience with cancer! I have always believed that a sense of humor is
vital to a healthy personality. I think I've never met a real fanatic,
religious or otherwise, who had a sense of humor. By "fanatic," I
mean a person so "hung up" on one cause or theory or pursuit as
to go to irrational extremes in that direction. Such a person sees all
of life in almost absolute, black-and-white terms. Whether lack of
a sense of humor is a cause or an effect of fanaticism, I'm not sure.
But I think it significant that the two almost always go together.

I had already learned of the healing power of a sense of humor
during the aftermath of the drowning of my father three years
previously. In fact, I had written an article called "Sunshine in a
House," which told of the healing power we found as sense of
humor and the ability to laugh gradually returned.

Later, I discovered that in his book, *Anatomy of An Illness*,
Norman Cousins, longtime editor of *Saturday Review*, confirmed
my instinctive feeling about the role of humor in the healing
process. Cousins undertook a unique battle to recover from a

collagen disease that was considered so likely to be fatal that doctors gave him one chance in five hundred to recover. [5]

Having been familiar with Hans Selye's book, *The Stress of Life,*[6] which dealt with the bad effects of negative emotions on body chemistry, Cousins reasoned: "If negative emotions produce chemical changes in the body, wouldn't positive emotions produce positive chemical changes? Is it possible that love, hope, faith, laughter, confidence, and the will to live have therapeutic value? Do chemical changes occur only on the downside?"[7]

These thoughts launched him on a unique program, with his doctor's cooperation, for mobilizing the resources of his own body and mind to effect healing. The success of his program is testified to by the fact that he not only recovered from the collagen disease and, later, from a massive heart attack, but also is now (as a layperson) senior lecturer at UCLA's School of Medicine and is a consulting editor for *Man and Medicine,* published at Columbia University.

Of course, his program consisted of much more than laughing, but the stimulation of good, happy feelings, was one of the cornerstones of his plan. He began by moving out of the hospital into a hotel room (thereby saving two thirds of the cost of a hospital room!) and proceeded, in his own words, to pursue "the full exercise of the affirmative emotions as a factor in enhancing body chemistry."[8]

He obtained a movie projector and some of Allen Funt's *Candid Camera* films, some old Marx Brothers films and a pile of humor books. He details the results:

> How scientific was it to believe that laughter—as well as positive emotions in general—was affecting my body chemistry for the better? If laughter did in fact have a salutary effect on the body's chemistry, it seemed at least theoretically likely that it would enhance the system's ability to fight the inflammation. So we took sedimentation rate readings just before as well as several hours after the laughter episodes. Each time, there was a drop of at least five points. The drop by itself was not substantial, but it held and was cumulative. I was greatly elated by the discovery that there is a physiologic basis for the ancient theory that laughter is good medicine.[9]

He also asserted:

> I made the joyous discovery that ten minutes of genuine belly laughter had an anesthetic effect and would give me at least two

hours of pain-free sleep. When the pain-killing effect of the laughter wore off, we would switch on the motion-picture projector again, and, not infrequently, it would lead to another pain-free sleep interval. [10]

Cousins' theory of the therapeutic value of laughter is reinforced by Dr. William Fry, associate clinical professor of psychiatry at Stanford University School of Medicine in California. Over the past twenty years he has monitored the physiologic effect of laughter on hundreds of people. He discovered that laughter reacts on the body just as exercise does, accelerating the heartbeat, increasing blood circulation and strengthening the cardiovascular system.

He says: "You contract your abdominal muscles during laughter, just as you do with sit-ups."[11]

He claims a good laugh ventilates the lungs, cleaning out the stale air and thus preventing moisture buildup and bacterial growth that causes infections.

In an issue of the magazine, *Woman's World*, he further claims that laughter is the best antidote for stress because it is "naturally followed by a period of relaxation and calm."[12]

Of special interest to me was his suggestion that laughter may even enhance cancer prevention by increasing the production of white blood cells, which play an active part in the body's defense against diseases.

I certainly experienced how laughter can relieve stress, when I was facing my cancer surgery. As I mentioned, we had to wait from a Wednesday, when I received the news, until the following Monday to see the surgeon. On the intervening Friday, my husband stopped at home to pick up his small Communion set. That triggered the first humorous incident—one I chuckled over often and told on every possible occasion, hoping I hadn't told it before to the same person.

To get the full impact, you have to know that I'm almost totally without a sense of direction. For a long time I carried around a cartoon of an ample lady, wedged into a roadside telephone booth, saying, "Operator, will you please trace this call and tell me where I am?."

On that Friday, seeing my husband's sad countenance when he stopped by, I said, "Cheer up! Nobody gets out of this life alive—but I'm not dead yet."

He turned and looked at me somberly, Communion kit in hand, and said, "I don't want you to go before I do."

Then, even before my eyes could get watery, a little grin touched his face and he added, "You have such a terrible sense of direction!"

I did a double take, then broke up, laughing so hard I set him off, too, and we stood there gasping and trying to catch our breath, only to go off into another helpless fit.

When we could speak again, I said, "Oh, I suppose you want to go along to be sure I'm headed in the right direction!"

"If you do go before me," he said, "I'm going to put a little piece of paper in the coffin with one word on it: 'UP.' "

That was good for another spurt of laughter and then he kissed me goodbye and was off, with a much more cheerful and hopeful expression on his face.

Some might think it a bit ghoulish to make a joke or get a laugh out of such a serious subject as death. All I can say is that the hearty laugh relieved the sense of tension and the aura of possibly impending doom. All during that weekend, whenever I told that story to friends, their surprised, spontaneous bursts of laughter found an echo in our own, for we had another laugh at every telling. We got a lot of therapeutic mileage out of that story, as did many others.

Even on the day of my entry into the hospital, I found an occasion for a good laugh—although I had to indulge in it all alone and wait for later to share it with my family. During the exam the internist gave me that first day, he pulled out an otoscope and peered into my ears. As he examined the right one, he said, "All OK—except there seems to be something in this one—a little wax, maybe?"

I put my finger in and felt a small, hard substance which I carefully removed. I knew in a flash what it was, opened my mouth, then shut it just in time to keep from blurting out the truth. It was from our oldest daughter, Barbara, that I learned the helpfulness of ear plugs to block out those sounds that keep rousing one from sleep: police and ambulance sirens, chiming clocks, low-flying airplanes, rowdy parties down the block. Barbara used small balls of moistened Kleenex. I thought Silly Putty would be ideal, but couldn't find any. However, I did find some Play-Doh and bought a box. The only trouble is that, exposed to air, it tends to harden and, when removed a crumbly, stiff portion will sometimes flake off into the ear. That's what the doctor had discovered.

I almost exclaimed, "Oh, that's just my Play-Doh." I caught myself just in time!

I could almost imagine the conversation in the doctors' lounge or at lunch, had I revealed the truth: "Sa-ay, I'll tell you a good one—I have an old gal up in 508 who puts Play-Doh in her ears!"

"Really? How odd! Is she—er...?"

"She seems rational enough. She has a daughter who's a nurse here up in the closed psych ward. You don't suppose...?"

Another occasion for a hearty laugh occurred about the fourth day after surgery. I was opening mail. One card struck me as so funny that, lying there all by myself, I started to laugh out loud. At that very moment, in walked the oncologist, coming to talk to me about the treatment they were recommending.

"Well!" he said, walking up to the bed. "You seem in excellent spirits, considering what you've just been through."

I handed him the card. "It's this," I said.

On the outside it read, "Hope your stay in the hospital..." and then on the inside it finished: "...is as short as your gown." And there was a picture of a funny-looking little old lady, bent over almost double, a look of frustrated embarrassment on her face as she tried vainly to pull a skimpy hospital gown down to a more modest length.

The doctor grinned widely and said, "Yeah, and now if they'd just figure out how to plug that gap in the back!"

As Dr. Fry, of Stanford, admonishes: "If something...funny happens, don't be afraid to cut loose and laugh with abandon...(it) has a feedback effect: the more you laugh, the better you feel, so you laugh even more and feel even better. As your mood improves, so does your health."[13]

When I looked into the Bible to see how Jesus handled people, I was struck by the initial words he often addressed to them. In Matthew 9:2, his first words to "a man sick of the palsy" were: "Son, be of good cheer." When the disciples were scared out of their wits at the approach of Jesus walking on the water, his first words were, "Be of good cheer" (Matthew 14:27). At the Last Supper, among the last words Jesus spoke to his disciples before he went to be crucified were these (right after he predicted their desertion of him!): "But be of good cheer; I have overcome the world" (John 16:33). I also noted one time that in the New Testament there are 366 "Fear not's"—one for every day of the year and one left over for good measure!

All I know is, the doctor had been planning to keep me at the hospital through the weekend, but about Wednesday he informed me that at the rate I was recovering, there was no reason I couldn't go home on Friday...and I did. Maybe laughter and a sense of humor played more of a part in my speedy, uncomplicated recovery than one might guess. That and hordes of praying friends seem an almost unbeatable combination.

9

Why Did God Let This Happen?

Thoughts on the Power, Love, and the Will of God

I FELT IN PRETTY GOOD SHAPE when I left the hospital and was eager to resume a normal life, but immediately I found that major surgery leaves you feeling like a rag after you're on your feet for about fifteen minutes! Therefore, I spent an amazing amount of time on the couch, resting. But inactivity leads to lots of thinking—at least in my case. I began thinking about questions that had been asked me before I went to the hospital.

On the Sunday between when I got the bad news on what my X-rays showed and my appointment with the surgeon, I had gone to church as usual and taught my adult Bible class. I told them the news and said I would not be teaching until further notice.

After church, a longtime member of the congregation came up to me, squeezed my hand and said, "Why? Why?" Another friend wrote from California, "My first reaction was, 'Why, God? Why her?'" This is a friend whom I met forty years ago and who recently told me that she has prayed for me every day for those forty years. I was utterly amazed and told her, "No wonder my life has been so beautiful!" Who could be brought daily before the throne of grace in that spirit of love and faithfulness and not have it "rub off" mightily on the person being prayed for?

These two women were asking the same question my husband and I have been asked many times during the years of our ministry: "Why do I have to have terminal cancer?" "Why does our only son have to die so young?" "Why are some Christians (sometimes it seems the "best" ones) afflicted with a long-drawn-out, deeply painful disease that seems to kill by inches?" "Why does this wonderful, young Christian mother, with a loving husband and children yet at home depending on her, have to die while some cruel, drunken father who beats his wife and children and endangers people's lives on the highway lives on and on? Why?"

I think we've all asked such questions—if not out loud, then deep within our own hearts. I know I certainly have! But up to now, with all the articles I've written, I never dared tackle these questions in print. I felt I would be stating only theory. I'd never been sick enough as an adult to feel I had any right to air views that had not been tested by my own experience. I felt that if I wrote some of the things I believed about God's will, anyone reading it might say, "Yes, that's easy for you to say! You haven't faced a life-threatening illness; you haven't even had to face the death of someone really close to you." And such a person would have been right. As I wrote to a friend concerning what I'd learned about the power of prayer, "I've been too healthy to learn some things!" But with the death of my father, to whom I was very close, and then in this current experience with cancer, I feel more confident about dealing in print with some of these knotty problems that begin with *why*.

In fact, I discovered I, too, was re-asking them when I found myself among those whose lives have been threatened by this killer disease, cancer. But I didn't feel guilty about asking God some questions. Some Christians think it is a sin to ask, "Why?" They say, "This affliction is from the hand of God. It's doubting God to ask why, and doubt is sin." Although I feel comfortable questioning God, I found out in a hurry that one question certainly leads to another. Before you know it, unless you are grounded in God's truth, everything is up for grabs.

I firmly believe that truth, if earnestly sought, will always emerge and will vindicate itself, and I've always been a questioner. So, I resolved to let my mind pose whatever questions it wanted, and then try to deal with them from a biblical basis.

For example, I, too, found myself wondering, *Why me, God?* Then I read an article in which the author in a similar situation said she asked herself, *Why not me?* I realized that the *why me?* question perhaps subtly concealed another question that consciously I might not want to acknowledge. Was I really asking, *Why, when I'm a good Christian, does this have to happen to me?* Was I, somewhere deep in my subconscious, harboring the idea that if I trusted in God and daily asked for guidance and protection, then I ought to be exempt from this sort of thing? If I weren't exempt, then what was the use of all that praying? Or perhaps that *why me?* question was hiding the kind of fear my aged mother expressed during some acute pain she was undergoing: "Maybe God is punishing me for something I've done. Maybe God is angry with me."

Being the analytical type, I just couldn't shrug off the problems that these thoughts brought to my mind. Despite my efforts to ignore what one might call the "theological implications" of my situation, I found myself mulling over those old, knotty problems of the relationship between God and suffering.

For instance, after the *why me?* question, I caught myself thinking, *If God is so loving, how can God permit anyone to suffer on and on? Wouldn't a loving God either heal such people or release them mercifully into a quick death?* This question has become even more painfully urgent at present because of my ninety-eight-year-old mother who, even with a still lucid mind, is lying bedridden, in much pain and praying to die. She's ready, she says...but still, she lies here, waiting, hoping.

The thought comes, *Maybe God can't do anything—maybe God is not all-powerful!* That is the theory of Rabbi Harold Kushner, who wrote *When Bad Things Happen to Good People.*[14] He claims you have to make a choice between God's love and God's omnipotence; for if God is both loving and omnipotent then God would not allow people to suffer. Kushner arbitrarily chooses to believe that God is therefore all-loving but not all-powerful.

I realized that, if I'm going to pick and choose what I believe about the nature of God, then what's to stop me from believing the opposite: that maybe God just doesn't care? Maybe God isn't loving. Maybe God just started everything going and then left us on our own!

If you follow this train of thought, the next logical questions would seem to be: Is God out there at all? Was Christ a fraud? A bemused idealist? Or did some of those disciples make up a lot of things about a very ordinary (but very personable and winning) man?

But if I believe the Bible, I thought, *then I accept what Jesus himself taught us: that God is love.* If the New Testament is clear about anything, it is shiningly clear that Jesus brought a message of the undying love of God for humankind, as expressed so beautifully in John 3:16. But also, the Bible teaches the omnipotence of God: God is the Creator who made everything there is. Jesus said, "...with God all things are possible" (Mark 10:27). In Revelation "the voice of a great multitude" hails the reign of "the Lord God omnipotent" (19:6). No, I certainly am not free to parcel out God's powers according to my own thinking—not if I stick with the idea that the Bible speaks the truth about God! *So,* I thought, *if God is all-loving and all-powerful, there must be some other reason why God does not wipe out all the suffering, particularly of those who are faithful followers. God obviously does not intervene most of the time: suffering, illness, and pain are rampant in our world.*

Incidentally, I would often get tired of this painstaking thinking (I was tired anyway, from the surgery and from trying to get back to normal in my daily life); but when my mortality became real to me, it made me think harder about these matters. So, on my next session on the couch I pursued this thinking, trying to find at least some partial answers that would satisfy me. Lying there, I pictured myself in a circle of God's love and then visualized God allowing cancer to penetrate that circle. *Why? Could those people be right who claim that everything comes directly from the hand of God and that I must thank God for this cancer?*

Again, I had to take recourse to the Bible—and I found that it plainly rejects such thinking. The New Testament tells us that God is not the author of evil. God does not sit on a throne and figure out which ones will be zapped today with what calamity. In fact, the Bible says just the opposite: that God is the author of every good and perfect gift (James 1:17).

I tried another road of thought: *Maybe what we label "bad" really isn't bad at all in God's view, but is really "good" in light of the fact that God's purpose is to make us better.* But, again, when I remembered the biblical accounts of Christ's life, I recalled that when confronted with illness and disease, Christ healed. He rebuked the devil in an insane man. He wept in the presence of death of loved ones. I realized that I must not only reject the idea that God is the author of bad things, but I must also reject the idea that what looks bad to me looks good to God. Our Creator evidently thought disease, insanity, and death were bad, just as I do. This put an end to the sort of outlook that says I must thank God for things like cancer!

But I discovered when going through the whole experience of having cancer that, although I felt it would border on blasphemy to thank God *for* the situation, I could (and did) give thanks *in* the situation for all the blessings that were part of the experience: for God's keeping the promises about upholding me and giving me strength—yes, even joy; for the gifted doctors and nurses who gave to me freely not only of their skills and knowledge but of their already taxed physical energies and their own personal concern; for my chance to witness to God's love and goodness, even while I was in this less-than-desirable situation. Didn't my Bible say that all things work together for good to those who love the Lord? This I found to be true, indeed.

Even so, we do have to admit, don't we, that "bad" things do happen to Christians. In other words, we at least have to say that God does not intervene to stop some of these illnesses, calamities, catastrophes. We do have to say that God lets them happen. Why? I finally decided that the answer is not a single, simplistic one; it's more like a web of interwoven "becauses."

First, I realized that I was forgetting or underestimating the force, power, and prevalence of evil. The Bible says that the Prince of Darkness rules this world. True, Jesus did say, "I have overcome the world." Nevertheless, Evil is still permitted to influence and have its way in this world wherever people allow it and are willing to let it be in control. For that reason, much evil runs rampant, and I believe that many times Christians are caught in the "fallout" of generations of corporate sin, including genetic defects, pollution, bad personal choices, etc. But that alone didn't totally satisfy me as an explanation of why God doesn't protect us from the results of such things (nor, indeed, why God allows Evil to have as much free reign as it does).

Then I began to think about how we are made and how our universe is arranged. One of the gifts God has given us is free will—although since the Fall, it, too, is under the dominion of sin. But, crippled as it is, it allows me to make choices. However, if I make unwise choices, certain bad results are bound to happen because of "the way things work." This "way things work" we sometimes call "natural law." For example, if I choose, I can load up on a diet too high in fats, sugar, salt—and run the risk of reaping cancer, diabetes, high blood pressure, heart trouble and a host of other major and minor ills. I know that before my cancer, I had not been eating as wisely as I do now. Periodic "crash" diets were stupid choices! I remember one that was high in fat and protein. I quit that one when I read that people were blaming it for heart attacks and strokes.

Whenever we make choices, certain predictable results are almost sure to follow. Notice that word "predictable." The fact that I can "predict" that certain results will almost always follow certain actions means that I am dealing with an orderly, reasonable, dependable environment which operates in predictable fashion.

I can buy that in general, I told myself—but isn't the Christian God supposed to be a God of miracles? Isn't God able to alter or circumvent the "natural law" which was set up by God in the first place? And aren't there many instances in the Bible (all the miracles) in which God did just that? Yes! Well, then, I wondered, why doesn't God do this for all Christians at all times? Does it all depend on the depth of a person's faith? If I were perfect in my trust in God, would I be spared from accidents, illnesses, cancer? Again, my Bible, when I pondered over it, pointed the way to some answers. (This was one of the good things about the cancer experience: I had to slow down, rest more often...and thus I had more time to think, to read, to study the Bible.)

In reading the Bible, I noticed that God does intervene sometimes to circumvent or alter the "normal" results of natural law. The apostle Paul, for instance, even though his conscience was pricking him horribly, plowed determinedly on toward Damascus to persecute the Christians there. If God had not literally knocked him down in the road and spoken directly to him, the "natural" course of events probably would have continued. Christianity would have lost its greatest promoter. In that case, God intervened almost overpoweringly.

On the other hand, the history of Christianity is replete with examples of people who were God's faithful followers, yet were not spared pain, suffering, or even violent deaths as martyrs. So I still can't answer the question as to why God intervenes sometimes and not others. I can only conclude that in the process of accomplishing divine will, God sometimes finds it necessary to intervene in the natural cause-effect pattern, but in most cases does not deem it wise to disrupt that pattern.

Another time on one of my couch breaks, I continued my thinking about why God cannot spare Christians from the natural disasters, sufferings, and pain of normal life. I tried to visualize the results on a worldwide basis if God saw to it that nothing bad ever happened to any of us. First, God would have to intervene, not now and then, but constantly with the natural laws of cause and effect. That would mean such a disruption of the order and predictability of life and nature that we would all be utterly disoriented. No one could count on anything for sure and, being human and unstable enough at best, we would probably end up as psychological wrecks. What a mockery such intervention would make of our free will!

And morality—the whole basis for an ethic grounded in the concepts of right and wrong—would be sabotaged. How, then, would we learn and grow? It would be as if a parent should say to a child, "Now you can do anything you want; the choices are all yours to make." But then, whenever the child made a bad choice or got into trouble, the parent would "pull strings" to extricate the child from any ill effects of that choice. How would the child learn? All concepts of right and wrong would be blurred or destroyed because all actions, whether bad or good would have a good outcome...thanks to intervention and manipulation by the parent. Then I tried to imagine how humankind would react if they knew God would keep all Christians from any bad experiences. Everybody would jump on the bandwagon just for the benefits, not from the motives Christ desires.

I remembered reading that when the first missionaries went to China, they got the poor people to listen to the gospel by giving them rice rations. Some people pretended to become Christians in order to get the food. They were called "rice Christians." In the New Testament I found that Christ was concerned with the same problem. More than once he ordered his disciples or those he healed not to tell anyone about his miracles. Besides the fact that his "time" had not come and he had to be safe to finish his mission, there was also the factor that he didn't want people to follow him just so that they would "get in on" his miracles. He wanted changed hearts!

As I regained my strength and slowly resumed my normal life, I felt that my "couch meditations" had strengthened my faith and clarified my own thinking about God's role as it relates to the suffering, pain and evil in human experience.

Basically, these are the conclusions I came to:

1. Appearances to the contrary notwithstanding, God is all-good, all-loving and all-powerful. I believe God's will toward us is good because Jesus said so, and I am convinced that Jesus is really who he said he is: God in the flesh, in the form of a human, who came here precisely to tell us who God is and what God is like. (Christ came in addition, of course, for the purpose of bringing us back into a right relationship with God through his life, death, and resurrection—the whole work of the atonement.)

2. For good and sound reasons (some of which we can surmise but some of which remain shrouded in mystery), God has not chosen to exempt Christians from the ills and sorrows that beset humankind in general. Two of these reasons are God's respect for and adherence to an orderly universe of cause and effect and a desire that we learn the relationship between our choices and the results that follow. Christians are part of this fallen world and, while we are given the power to overcome and to live above the traps and goals of that fallen world, we must still share in its workings and burdens, even as Christ did. Therefore, we ought not to follow the false path of thinking that as Christians we ought to be exempt from "all that." Peter admonished: "My dear friends, do not be surprised at the painful test you are suffering, as though something unusual were happening to you. Rather be glad that you are sharing Christ's sufferings, so that you may be full of joy when his glory is revealed" (1 Peter 4:12, GNB). I in no way interpret this to mean that God causes bad things to happen to us. James tells us: "If a person is tempted by such trials, he must not say, 'This temptation comes from God.' For God cannot be tempted by evil, and he himself tempts no one" (James 1:13, GNB).

3. On the other hand, God does choose on occasion to supersede "natural law" and produce a miracle—but only when and where God chooses and for God's own reasons, which are often a mystery to us.

4. Finally, I believe (and this is probably the most important point of all) that anything that happens to us who are Christian can be used to glorify God, to strengthen our faith, to perfect us in discipleship and to help us witness to an unbelieving world. I believe that if this is our true desire in all that happens to us, that

desire itself produces in us the very wonderful attitude and climate that is the most powerful tool in healing of body, mind and spirit. More and more I was learning that I could trust the mercy and power of the one true God, whom we know through Jesus Christ. Through Christ, the Word made flesh, I grew in confidence that God loves us and that God's will for us is always for good. The *whys*, the mysteries of God's ways will always remain. Fortunately, God is not limited to my understanding. What I do know of my Creator, through Christ, gives me courage and confidence to trust beyond the bounds of my own knowledge, even when I must walk from sunshine into the midnight of sorrow, suffering...even death.

And so, during all the ordeal of surgery, then the recuperation at home, I had not only the assurance that many were caring and praying, but also the calm certainty that through it all, I had been and would continue to be in the care of the God of love.

10

Strengthening the Odds

BEFORE I LEFT THE HOSPITAL, one of the oncologists talked to me, describing what he called "preventive chemotherapy." He said that according to statistics colon cancer patients have a fifty-fifty chance that it will not recur. But with the preventive therapy, the odds of its not recurring increase to as high as eighty-five percent. I also learned that a hospital in Texas was, at that time, the only other hospital engaged in this particular program, which was designed not only to give the preventive chemotherapy, but at the same time to "up" the immune system of the patient. The doctor concluded by saying it was entirely up to me whether to undergo the treatment.

After discussing it with my husband, I decided to enter the program. The chemotherapy itself was administered in the form of a liquid dripped slowly into a vein in my wrist once a month for six months. This part of the program produced a drastic reaction, even though Sharon, the oncologist's nurse-assistant, said most people do not have a reaction to it. However, my stomach has a reputation for reacting petulantly to whatever else is wrong with me—a strange situation for someone who can (and does!) eat practically anything with no ill effects. My father, a physician, used to say, "Betty throws up if she gets a hangnail!" Thus, after each chemotherapy treatment, I would barely arrive home before becoming violently ill, vomiting every fifteen to twenty minutes for about six hours. The doctors tried everything: giving me anti-nausea pills to take before arriving; doubling the time it took to drip the medication into the vein...but nothing helped. The reaction had to run its course.

Then, usually about 8 P.M., the sickness would abruptly subside as if someone had pushed a button. The next day I always felt a bit dragged out, but could eat normally and felt just fine the remainder of the month. I dreaded those monthly treatments—but I figured that a total of about thirty-six hours of discomfort, spread over a six-month period, for only six hours at a time, was well worth it in terms of the improved chance of not getting cancer again. The second part of the program, designed to strengthen the immune system, was administered twice a month for the first three months. A liquid containing an inactivated tubercle bacillus was painted on a small area of my upper back and then scraped into my skin by an instrument with sharp, needle-like projections. It did indeed hurt, but not for long, because Sharon's philosophy was that it's better to scrape away quickly and get it over with than to prolong the agony. I agreed!

One time the oncologist walked past while Sharon was per-forming this mini-torture. He gave a slight shudder and said, "I'm glad I don't have to do those!" Sharon whispered, "He's so tenderhearted!"

Besides stimulating the immune system, this treatment also makes one's back look like that of a torture victim. During that first summer after the surgery when we left for vacation at our cabin in Wisconsin, my back was still criss-crossed with scars, although that part of the treatment was over. One day when my husband and I were swimming down by our dock, we noticed that our neighbor was at his dock for the first time that year. We waded over to greet him, chatted a few moments, then turned back to our own area.

As I turned to wade out into deeper water, my husband said, "Good heavens, your back! I wonder what he thought when he got a view of that! I bet he thinks I'm in the habit of beating you!"

After six of those treatments over a three-month period, I re-ceived the medicine as a drink, diluted in orange juice, for the next nine months. When we went on vacation that summer, the oncologist ordered the medication, frozen in orange juice, to be administered to me at a clinic in the town near our cabin. This portion of the treatment was painless, with no side effects.

I have grown to realize and appreciate anew the God-given role that modern medicine, with its roster of dedicated personnel, plays in the life of our society. To me it is no less wonderful that God has supplied the wherewithal for many kinds of healing; that God has gifted men and women with the knowledge, desire, and power to bring healing to humankind. Indeed, this whole experience has increased my faith in the God I have learned to know through Jesus Christ. God's promises to uphold and strengthen and never forsake, all have been kept.

The truth of Simone Weil's observation quoted earlier in the book has truly been validated in my life:

> It is only from the light which streams constantly from heaven that a tree can derive energy to strike its roots deep in the soil. The tree is, in fact, rooted in the sky. [15]

I, this earthly creature, my feet planted on the soil of earth, can survive spiritually only if I am "rooted in the sky," basking in that Light streaming constantly into my soul with God's heavenly nourishment of love. "Rooted and grounded" in that love, I then have the power "to comprehend with all the saints what is the breadth and length and height and depth, and to know the love of Christ" (Ephesians 3:17-19, RSV).

Surviving physically is not the number-one priority with me; I can hold the blessing of my human life in an open hand, not clutching it in fear, not daunted by the prospect that eventually I must relinquish it.

Surviving spiritually is the number-one priority. But here, too, I need have no fear. I have been assured by my Lord, in the Bible's recorded words, that nothing can snatch me out of God's hand nor separate me from God's love. To dwell in that love forever—that is the glorious goal, the prize, the crown, compared to which all the suffering of this life becomes as nothing. It seems to me that this promise of eternal glory, made with such assurance by One who claimed to be no less than a human appearance of God Almighty, ought to be taken most seriously by anyone who really wants to know what life is all about!

Epilogue

IT NOW HAS BEEN over five-and-a-half years since my cancer surgery.

During these five years, even after the chemotherapy was finished, I have been thoroughly monitored, although the frequency of the very thorough checkups has decreased from once every two months to once a year now. My oncologist, a most humane and caring man, told me at the beginning: "We'll monitor you for the rest of your life—and if I die first, I'll hand you over to someone else!" He had also said, "You are going to be one of my cures." I was happy that he used the word "cure." Usually doctors talk in terms of "remission," subtly communicating the idea that it's only a matter of time until the ax will fall again!

I do consider myself "cured." After all, no sign of cancer has appeared for over five years. If I should ever get that disease again I would consider it a new ailment.

What about my life now? The insights I gained have remained, enriching my days. For me, the most important result of that whole experience has been the continuing sense of God's nearness. Perhaps anyone who is trying to live the Christian life tends to feel the reality and nearness of God as he or she grows older, but I think my bout with cancer hastened and intensified that sense of God's closeness.

Another result has been a heightened sense of the shortness and unpredictability of this life. We so often think in terms of an indefinite life span. We tend not to realize that life could be snuffed out in a moment. I am not morbid about this; it has just become a part of my awareness. I find myself frequently conscious of the "permanent abiding place" that awaits all those who belong to the Lord. In fact, I read often a prayer from Leslie Weatherhead's *Salute to a Sufferer* taped above my writing table. It encompasses so well my own feelings and hopes about my earthly life and the eternal one to come:

O God, who dwells in unapproachable mystery and whose ways are far beyond our understanding, help us to rest our minds in the certainty that we are dear to you in spite of all our weaknesses and failures. Forgive us if, sometimes, suffering fills all our horizon and we find no comfort in any word of man or any thought of you. Draw very near to us in the tenderness and compassion which overflowed from you into the heart of Christ, and, for his sake, keep alive the flickering flame of our faith, hope and love. Show us the pathway of your will for us in each day and in each circumstance.

If it may be, lighten our burden, gladden our eyes, comfort our hearts, heal the sick body, and quiet the troubled mind. But whatever may lie ahead, give us the assurance that your friendliness enwraps us, that a wondrous purpose that cannot be defeated is being worked out in our lives, and that nothing can ever snatch us from your loving care.

So, at last, without regret and without dishonor, bring us to our journey's end in peace. Amen. [16]

The unpredictability of the life span and that sense of God's nearness keep me in a balance that minimizes fear and maximizes the sense of peace, hope and joy. Thus, while I have great zest for this life, still, five-and-a-half years after that faith-strengthening experience of going through a life-threatening illness, I am always aware that I am "rooted in the sky."

Betty Garton Ulrich
August 1988

Notes

Quotations

[1] Simone Weil. The author was unable to locate the specific source for this quote. If that information is provided, the publisher would be happy to include it in any future editions.

Chapter 1

[2] James Boswell, *Boswell's Life of Samuel Johnson*, edited by Anne and Irvin Ehrenpreis. (New York: Washington Square Press, Inc., 1965).

Chapter 6

[3] Elisabeth Kubler-Ross, *On Death and Dying*, (New York: Macmillan Publishing Company, 1969).

Chapter 8

[4] Sydney Smith in *The New Dictionary of Thoughts*, rev. ed., ed. Tryon Edwards (New York: Doubleday & Co., Inc., 1955).
[5] Norman Cousins, *Anatomy of an Illness As Perceived by the Patient*, (New York: W.W. Norton and Company, 1979).
[6] Hans Selye, *The Stress of Life*, (New York: McGraw-Hill, Inc., 1978).
[7] Cousins, pp.34-35.
[8] Ibid., p.39.
[9] Ibid., p.40.
[10] Ibid., pp. 39-40.
[11] William Fry, M.D., "Laughter: the Best Medicine," *Woman's World*, May 17, 1983.
[12] Ibid.
[13] Ibid.

Chapter 9

[14] Harold S. Kushner, *When Bad Things Happen to Good People,* (New York: Schocken Books, Inc., 1981).

Chapter 10

[15] Simone Weil. See Note 1.

Epilogue

[16] Leslie D. Weatherhead, *Salute to a Sufferer,* (Nashville: Abingdon Press, 1962), p.95.